margaret Tempest.

WATER-RAT'S PICNIC

Uniform with this volume:

SQUIRREL GOES SKATING
WISE OWL'S STORY
LITTLE GREY RABBIT'S PARTY
THE KNOT SQUIRREL TIED
FUZZYPEG GOES TO SCHOOL
LITTLE GREY RABBIT'S CHRISTMAS
MOLDY WARP THE MOLE
LITTLE GREY RABBIT'S WASHING DAY
WATER RAT'S PICNIC
LITTLE GREY RABBIT'S BIRTHDAY
THE SPECKLEDY HEN
LITTLE GREY RABBIT AND THE WEASELS
GREY RABBIT AND THE WANDERING HEDGEHOG
LITTLE GREY RABBIT MAKES LACE
HARE AND THE EASTER EGGS
LITTLE GREY RABBIT'S VALENTINE
LITTLE GREY RABBIT GOES TO SEA
HARE AND GUY FAWKES
LITTLE GREY RABBIT'S PAINT BOX
GREY RABBIT FINDS A SHOE
GREY RABBIT AND THE CIRCUS
GREY RABBIT'S MAY DAY
HARE GOES SHOPPING
LITTLE GREY RABBIT'S PANCAKE DAY
LITTLE GREY RABBIT TO THE RESCUE
HARE JOINS THE HOME GUARD
LITTLE GREY RABBIT GOES TO THE NORTH POLE

LITTLE GREY RABBIT'S PAINTING BOOK

LITTLE GREY RABBIT'S SONG BOOK
Words by Alison Uttley
Music by David Davis
Published by Ascherberg, Hopwood & Crew Ltd.
16 Mortimer Street, London, W.1

Water - Rat's Picnic

by Alison Uttley
Pictures by Margaret Tempest

Collins, 14 St. James's Place London

First Impression	October 1943
Second Impression	April 1944
Third Impression	September 1946
Fourth Impression	August 1947
Fifth Impression	April 1949
Sixth Impression	January 1950
Seventh Impression	May 1951
Eighth Impression	April 1955
Ninth Impression	May 1962
Tenth Impression	March 1969
Eleventh Impression	January 1972

ISBN 0 00 194110 0

COPYRIGHT
PRINTED IN GREAT BRITAIN
COLLINS CLEAR-TYPE PRESS: LONDON AND GLASGOW

FOREWORD

Of course you must understand that Grey Rabbit's
home had no electric light or gas, and even the candles
were made from pith of rushes dipped in wax from the
wild bees' nests, which Squirrel found. Water there was
in plenty, but it did not come from a tap. It flowed from
a spring outside, which rose up from the ground and
went to a brook. Grey Rabbit cooked on a fire, but it
was a wood fire, there was no coal in that part of the
country. Tea did not come from India, but from a
little herb known very well to country people, who
once dried it and used it in their cottage homes. Bread
was baked from wheat ears, ground fine, and Hare and
Grey Rabbit gleaned in the cornfields to get the wheat.

The doormats were plaited rushes, like country-made
mats, and cushions were stuffed with wool gathered from
the hedges where sheep pushed through the thorns. As
for the looking-glass, Grey Rabbit found the glass,
dropped from a lady's handbag, and Mole made a frame
for it. Usually the animals gazed at themselves in the
still pools as so many country children have done. The
country ways of Grey Rabbit were the country ways
known to the author.

ONE DAY WATER-RAT came out of his house by the river-side and strolled down his garden path. The garden was full of river-bank flowers, bright blue forget-me-nots, water-mint, and yellow flags. He picked a sprig of flowering-rush and fastened it in his buttonhole. Then he whistled a sea shanty and went towards his boat-house.

There lay the neatest, prettiest little boat you ever saw! She had a pair of slender oars like scarlet wings. She was made of polished elm, and the name, the " Saucy Nancy," was picked out in gold letters. A couple of cushions lay on the seat, and a water-jar was in the bow.

WATER-RAT was very proud of his boat. " She's the tightest, trimmest little craft on the river," he boasted to his friends, and they popped their heads out of their doorways and nodded. Nobody had a boat like Water-rat's.

On this particular fine day Water-rat took a duster from his pocket and whisked the specks from the boat. Then he stepped back and looked at her with admiration. He took the stone jar to the spring and filled it with clear water. He polished up the copper kettle and packed the picnic basket.

"WHERE MIGHT YOU BE GO-ING to-day, Sir?" asked Mrs. Webster, his stout housekeeper.

"I'm going to see some young friends of mine, Mrs. Webster," said Water-rat. "I shall try to persuade them to join me in a water-picnic. They've never seen a boat, I believe." He laughed happily and shook his white frills.

"Then they'll have a surprise when they see the 'Saucy Nancy', Sir. Ain't she a beauty? Do you want anything more to eat, Sir? Have you got your pocket handkerchief, Sir, and the matches?"

THE GOOD HOUSEKEEPER nodded and curtseyed and then retired to clean the narrow passages and the rooms of Water-rat's house.

Water-rat settled himself in the boat, and paddled peacefully upstream. Swallows flew over his head, dipped to the water and then sped away. " Fine day, Ratty," they twittered. " Good luck to your voyage," and Water-rat cried, " Same to you, Swallows."

Green Dragon-flies darted here and there, and a King-fisher shot by like an arrow. Among the reeds at the water's edge a brown Water-hen was busy with a heap of washing. Water-rat rested a moment to watch her.

"A GOOD DRYING-DAY," said he, and the Water-hen looked up from her work. She hung Water-rat's shirt on a bent bulrush, and draped his frills over the reeds. She was the little laundress, you may remember.

"The ducks are very tiresome," she told Water-rat. "They tease me, and carry off the washing, and I have no peace." She sighed and shook her little tail.

"Never mind. You've got a fine young family to help you," said Water-rat. A crowd of fluffy water-chicks danced on the ripples and flashed their gossamer scarves at him.

"FOURTEEN children," said the Water-hen, proudly, "and every one of them is a champion swimmer! "

Water-rat took up the oars and rowed some distance. He moored the boat to the roots of a willow and leapt out. Then he walked across the fields to Grey Rabbit's house. His short legs ached as he went up the garden, for he was a water animal and field paths tired him. He tapped at the door.

"Come in! Come in! " called Grey Rabbit, who was busy making strawberry jam.

"OH, WATER-RAT! How pleased I am to see you!" she cried when she saw her friend. "Do sit down and rest. I shan't be long now. The strawberries are bubbling."

"Nice smell," said Water-rat, sinking into the rocking-chair and wiping his forehead. "We have no strawberries by the river."

"What kind of jam do you make?" asked Grey Rabbit.

"Lily-bud jam," said Water-rat. "Mrs. Webster makes it from the lilies in our backwater."

GREY RABBIT LADLED THE JAM into a row of little glass jars. She covered each with a strawberry leaf and tied it with a blade of grass.

" That's finished! " She sat down by Water-rat and fanned her hot face.

" I came to invite you and Squirrel to go for a picnic," said Water-rat. "My boat is moored by the old willow, and the food is aboard."

" A picnic! A boat! " cried little Grey Rabbit, clapping her hands.

" A boat? A real live boat? " called Squirrel, dancing in on tiptoes.

" A picnic? A real live picnic? " shouted Hare, popping his head in at the window.

" I'm afraid my boat will only hold three," said Water-rat coldly.

16

"THAT'S ALL RIGHT," said Hare. "You can swim alongside, Water-rat. You are a fine swimmer."

"There would be nobody to row, Hare. Besides, you are too big. You would capsize my 'Saucy Nancy.'"

Hare frowned and stamped his foot. He came into the room and stood in front of Water-rat.

"Look here," he cried. "Do you mean to say you are going on a picnic without me? It's impossible! I've never been left out! I'm the life and soul of *every* party. What is there to eat, Water-rat?"

"EGG-AND-CRESS SANDWICHES marigold sponge, watermint jellies, lobster patties——"

" Stop! Stop! " moaned Hare, wiping his eyes. " This is too much. This will be the death of me! I shall never get over the shock! Never! "

He sank half-fainting on a chair, and Grey Rabbit and Squirrel hastened to loosen his collar. Little Grey Rabbit fetched a glass of primrose wine, and he sipped it with little groans. Then he peeped to see the effect upon Water-rat.

" Poor Hare! " sighed Grey Rabbit. " Poor dear Hare."

" I'M AFRAID WE CAN'T GO,
Water-rat. We can't leave Hare
behind," said Squirrel.

" I have a plan." Water-rat spoke
rather crossly.

" Yes? What is it? " they asked,
and Hare opened wide his eyes and
forgot to faint.

" Surely you could run faster than
the ' Saucy Nancy,' Hare? Suppose
you race along the river-bank while I
row Grey Rabbit and Squirrel. Then
you can choose the place for the picnic,
and we will all have a feast under the
trees."

" Ah! That's a good idea! " said
Hare. " I much prefer to run along
the bank. It isn't the boat I want, but
the picnic."

"THAT'S SETTLED." Water-rat breathed again.

Hare and Squirrel went upstairs to get ready and Grey Rabbit hastened after them, to tie Squirrel's bows and brush Hare's coat.

"I shall wear my goloshes because it might be wet on the river," said she.

"I shall take my fishing-net," said Hare.

"I shall have my new sunshade," said Squirrel, and she unfurled her little sunshade and shook its silken cover.

THEY SHUT the windows and locked the door and put the key under the mat. Grey Rabbit carried a pot of strawberry jam, Hare his fishing-net, and Squirrel the pretty little sunshade.

They tripped along by Water-rat's side, asking questions about the boat.

" Oh! How beautiful! " cried Grey Rabbit, when she saw the " Saucy Nancy " under the willow branches.

" You shall steer, Grey Rabbit," said Water-rat, " and Squirrel shall sit on a cushion."

HE HELPED THEM BOTH into the boat, and untied the rope.

" Look at the waves, and the darting fishes, and the green weeds! " cried Grey Rabbit. She jumped with excitement as she saw the water so near.

Squirrel twirled her sunshade, and spread out her tail. She glanced at her reflection in the clear river and dabbled with her paw.

" Oh! Oh! " she cried. " A fish has bitten me! Oh! I didn't know fish could bite."

" Yes," warned Water-rat. " They like a dainty morsel."

"GOOD-BYE. GOOD-BYE," called Hare. "I shall meet you soon. Take care of the food and don't fall in the river."

He galloped along the bank and they waved their paws to him. Soon he was out of sight.

Squirrel leaned over the side to watch the fish playing hide and seek under the boat's shadow. Grey Rabbit steered past small rocks and islands. Water-rat rowed with light, graceful sweeps of the scarlet oars. He pointed out many strange sights of the water highway.

THEY SAW A GREEN FROG sitting among the water-buttercups with a little fishing-rod and a woven bag to hold his catch. They saw the untidy house where the blue Kingfisher lived, and the neat cottages of the Water-rats.

They looked through the doorway of a Sand-martin's house and spoke to the mother and her brood. They stopped to chat with the Water-hen, and they admired the fourteen little chicks which swam squeaking round the boat.

THE LITTLE WATER-HENS scrambled along the oars and climbed on Grey Rabbit's knee. They showed her their gossamer scarves, and they poked their beaks in her apron pocket.

" Come away, you naughty children," scolded their mother. " Don't go worrying Grey Rabbit and Mister Water-rat."

" We love them," said Grey Rabbit, and she gave them some biscuits and stroked their tiny brown heads before she lifted them back into the water.

THERE WAS A SCURRY and flurry and a loud quacking as a flock of white Ducks came hurrying up.

" Dear me! " cried the Water-hen. " Here they are again! Come away, children. Come away! "

The Ducks swam up to the boat, diving and pushing.

" Where are you landlubbers going so fast? " they asked.

" For a picnic," said Water-rat. " Don't come too near! You shake my boat."

ONE DUCK snatched Squirrel's sunshade and carried it off with peals of quacking laughter. Another pulled the strings of Grey Rabbit's apron and untied it before poor Grey Rabbit could protest. Water-rat sprang up, but another Duck grabbed his frill. The Duck swam away with the little blue apron draped on her shoulders. Another twitched the ribbon from Squirrel's tail, and a fourth seized the pot of strawberry jam. There was such a commotion, such a rocking of the boat, and flash of feathers, and splash of water, that nobody noticed another Duck seize the picnic basket.

OH! " cried Grey Rabbit. " My little pot of jam! "

" Oh! My sunshade! " cried Squirrel, pointing to the Duck which swam holding the gay sunshade aloft.

" And Grey Rabbit's apron," cried Water-rat, pointing to the Duck which wore the blue apron on its snowy back.

" And Water-rat's frill, and Squirrel's ribbon," said Grey Rabbit, pointing to the Ducks with the white frill and the little blue ribbon.

' IT IS OUTRAGEOUS! " exclaimed Water-rat. Then he started. " What is that I see? " He stared at one of the Ducks. " Is it——? Can it be——? Is it possible? Has she taken the picnic basket? "

The Duck held the little basket, and tried to open it. She couldn't unfasten the wooden pin, and as she struggled the basket slipped and went down, down, down to the bottom of the river.

" Oh! Oh! " cried Squirrel and Grey Rabbit.

"I'LL GET IT!" muttered Water-rat, and he took off his velvet coat and dived overboard. Down to the bed of the river he went, and there, lying among the waterweeds, he found the basket. He put his arms round it, and swam back to the boat. He hauled it over the side and clambered after it.

Then he sat upon it, and rowed as fast as he could away from the Ducks. They were so busy playing with Grey Rabbit's apron, twirling the little sunshade, and eating the strawberry jam, they took no more notice of the boat.

"Lucky it's lined with mackintosh," said Water-rat.

"ALL MY THINGS are waterproof as I live by the river. It won't be any the worse, but I'm sorry about your apron, Grey Rabbit, and your sunshade, Squirrel."

" I will make another apron," said Grey Rabbit, cheerfully.

" And I will have one of those big round leaves for a sunshade if you will pick it for me, Water-rat," said Squirrel.

Water-rat picked the lily-leaf, and Squirrel held it over her head and tried to forget her sunshade.

" Where's Hare? " asked Water-rat, staring at the river bank. " He ought to be somewhere waiting for us. I'm hungry. It's time we had our picnic."

"COO-OO," called Grey Rabbit. "Coo-oo, Hare."

"Coo-oo," came a faint reply, but there was nobody to be seen. Water-rat pulled the boat to the shore, and looked around. From out of the reeds peered Hare, his coat torn, his net broken.

"Oh, dear!" he cried. "I've been chased by a dog and pestered by rabbits, and tossed by a bull and bitten by gnats. Oh dear! And you've been rowing peacefully on the river."

"Not so peacefully," laughed Grey Rabbit, as she climbed to the bank, and ran to meet Hare. "I've lost my blue apron, Hare."

"And I've lost my sunshade," added Squirrel, leaping lightly out of the boat.

"AND WE NEARLY LOST the picnic basket," said Water-rat.

"That would have been a calamity," muttered Hare. "A cal-cal-calamity! The thought of the picnic basket kept me from despair."

He took the basket from Water-rat and clasped it to his heart. Then he sat down under the silver birch trees to nurse it. Now and then he peeped through the meshes, or tried to unfasten the catch, but the basket was tightly shut.

Grey Rabbit and Squirrel ran about picking up sticks, and Water-rat carried the kettle and water-jar to the hollow by the trees.

"Pile up the wood! Make a big fire!" called Hare, and they heaped the sticks ready.

"NOW for the matches," said Water-rat, and he took the box out of its mackintosh cover and struck a light. The fire crackled, and yellow flames shot up.

"Come along, Hare. You have more breath than any of us. You can be the blow-bellows," said Squirrel, as she balanced the kettle on the top.

"Chased by gnats, bitten by a dog, pestered by a bull," murmured Hare, "and then they make me a blow-bellows."

He puffed out his cheeks and blew like the wind. Soon the kettle began to sing in its high shrill voice.

"WHAT DOES IT SAY?" asked Squirrel, leaning over to listen. " I'm nearly boiling. I'm nearly boiling. I'm quite boiling. Take me off! " said Water-rat. " That's what it says."

He unfastened the picnic basket and spread out the dainties. Grey Rabbit and Squirrel gave little shrieks of admiration as they took the three blue mugs, three blue plates and three tin spoons from the fitted basket. Hare leapt for joy when he saw the patties and sandwiches and jellies in the mackintosh wrappers.

" But where's Grey Rabbit's little mug? " he asked. " You've forgotten Grey Rabbit," he scolded Water-rat.

THEY ALL LOOKED at the three mugs planted among the daisies. " One for Water-rat, and one for Grey Rabbit, and one for me," said Squirrel.

" I'm going to drink from a water-lily," said Grey Rabbit quickly. "I've never had a water-lily cup in all my life."

Water-rat gave her a grateful glance and ran down to the river. He picked a yellow lily and she drank her tea from it.

What a feast there was! They laughed and sang and told their adventures, and quite forgot their troubles. Hare was very hungry, for, he explained, he had run for miles, while they had been resting in the boat.

41

I WAS CHASED by a rabbit, and tossed by a gnat, and bitten by a bull," said he, as he took the last sandwich.

" Bitten by a bulrush, you mean," said Water-rat.

" This is very nice jelly, Water-rat. I'm glad you rescued it from the watery grave," said Hare, and he finished off the water-mint jelly.

They took the cups to the river edge and washed them and dried them on the grasses. They hunted in the moss for the little tin spoons, and they repacked the basket. Then they sat down among the buttercups and daisies to watch the river whirling below them.

HARE CREPT SOFTLY out of sight, and climbed into the boat. He untied the rope and pushed her out into the stream.

"You didn't know I could row," he called, splashing with the scarlet oars. "It's quite easy."

"Oh, Hare! Take care!" shrieked Squirrel, as the boat rocked dangerously. "Sit down, Hare," commanded Water-rat. "You'll upset her if you stand up."

"YOUR BOAT IS SO WOBBLY," said Hare, swaying to one side. "If I move she rocks like a cradle. Steady on there! Steady!"

He sat down with a thump, and the boat shook. He dipped the oars deep in the river and dragged up some weeds. Then the oars waved wildly, Hare's feet flew up, and he shot backward into the water.

"Save me! Save me! I'm drowning!" he cried, kicking and struggling.

OUT OF THE SHADOWS came the company of Ducks, one with the blue apron over her shoulders, another with the red sunshade above her head, a third with a white frill around her neck, and the fourth with a ribbon in her beak.

They circled round poor Hare, and grabbed him by his fur. One got his left ear, and another his right, another his leg and the fourth his coat tail. Then they swam to the shore with him.

"THANKS FOR THE STRAW-BERRY JAM," they quacked as they pushed him on the bank, and away they went cackling with laughter.

Squirrel and Grey Rabbit dried him with their handkerchiefs and squeezed the water out of his fur. The poor bedraggled Hare crouched over the embers of the fire, shivering.

"It's very wet in the river," he said, with his teeth chattering. "I never knew that boat wasn't safe. Water-rat should never have invited us. We shall all be drowned going home!"

"YOU WILL HAVE TO RUN,"
said Grey Rabbit. "It will keep
you from catching cold."

"Chased by gnats, tossed by dogs,
worried by bulls," muttered Hare, "and
half-drowned on the top of it. That's
a water-picnic."

Water-rat swam after the little boat
and the pair of oars which were float-
ing down the river. He rowed back,
and dried the boat and wiped the
cushions.

"I TOLD YOU how it would be," said Hare sternly. "You would bring your old boat for the picnic. It isn't safe! It never ought to be on the river."

"What you want is a paddle-steamer," grunted Water-rat. "A paddle-steamer, with a captain and crew and life-belts."

"Yes," agreed Hare. "That's what I want. I'm going home! I feel a chill in my bones."

He started off along the river bank, trotting with head bent.

THE OTHERS seated themselves in the boat, but Water-rat turned to Grey Rabbit.

"Would you like to see my house, Grey Rabbit?" he asked. "It is quite near, and my housekeeper, Mrs. Webster, will be pleased to welcome you. There's watercress growing in my stream, and I will give you some to take home."

Grey Rabbit and Squirrel were delighted, and Water-rat turned the boat up the stream and stopped at the boathouse at the bottom of his garden.

He showed the wondering little land-animals his canoe and punt, secure in the small harbour.

THEN THEY WALKED up the garden path and Water-rat held aside the rushes which screened his front door from prying eyes. They entered the damp little house. In the hall hung Water-rat's fishing rods and nets, and a glass case containing a stuffed goldfish.

On a table stood an aquarium with shells and duck-weed, and sticklebacks and minnows.

" Chirrup!   Chirrup! "   whistled Water-rat, and the tiny fish came swimming to the side of the tank and held up their noses.

SQUIRREL could hardly tear herself away from this watery scene, but Water-rat led the way to the parlour. It was very wet, and Grey Rabbit was glad she had her goloshes. Squirrel tucked her feet high as she sat on the bulrush chair.

Water-rat tinkled a glass bell and Mrs. Webster came trotting in. Grey Rabbit and Squirrel smiled at the stout old Water-rat, with her frilled muslin apron, and little mob cap, and she curtseyed to them.

"MRS. WEBSTER, will you bring some of your water-lily jam for my guests?" asked Water-rat.

"Certainly, Sir. Please, Sir, the Water-hen has brought back your washing, and she is very sorry, Sir, but the Ducks carried off your handkerchiefs as they lay bleaching on the bank."

"Never mind, Mrs. Webster. They are up to their pranks to-day. But I'm fond of their comical ways. We have many a game together on summer evenings diving for minnows."

Mrs. Webster fetched the little pots of lily jam, and packed them in a bag for Grey Rabbit to carry.

"I'll get the watercress," said Water-rat. "Stay and talk to my friends, Mrs. Webster," and he hurried away.

56

"OH, MISS GREY RABBIT!" cried Mrs. Webster. "I am glad to see you! I've heard about you, how you shut that old Weasel in the oven! And you, Miss Squirrel! I heard how you tied a knot in that savage Rat's tail! I don't know how you dared!"

"Nor I," murmured Squirrel.

"How is Mister Hare? I suppose he couldn't go to the picnic, being too big for the boat?"

"Oh dear!" cried Grey Rabbit. "I'd forgotten about him! He fell in the river, Mrs. Webster. We must hurry home."

"HUM! ALWAYS DOING SOME-THING, Mister Hare. Played noughts and crosses with the Fox, didn't he?" Mrs. Webster smoothed her apron placidly.

Water-rat came padding back with the basket of green cresses.

"We must go home," said Grey Rabbit as she thanked him. "Poor Hare is waiting for us, all wet."

"Good-bye, Mrs. Webster. Good-bye," they called as they hurried away. Water-rat rowed swiftly, and soon they were back at the old willow tree.

"THANK YOU, DEAR WATER-RAT. Thank you," they said, and they scampered home as fast as they could.

"Hare! Hare!" they called as they went into the house. "Guess what we did! We went to Water-rat's house, and we saw a stuffed goldfish, and a canoe, and—Hare, where are you?"

A violent sneeze shook the house and loud bangs came from Hare's bedroom.

They ran upstairs. There was Hare with his feet in mustard and water and his head in a blanket.

" ATISHOO! " sneezed Hare. " I thought you were both drowned! Make me some elder-flower tea, Grey Rabbit, and make me some gruel with sugar in it, Squirrel. Quick! Atishoo! "

Squirrel and Grey Rabbit raced round with herbs and hot water, and soon Hare was snug in bed with his basin of gruel and teapot of elder-flower tea.

" Now tell me all about it," said he.

So little Grey Rabbit began to tell of Mrs. Webster, and the aquarium. Her silvery little voice went on with her tale, but Hare shut his eyes. He was lulled by the sound, and before she had finished he was fast asleep.

SHE TIPTOED downstairs, and joined Squirrel, who was resting by the fire.

Pit-pat! Pit-pat! Pit-pat! Little footsteps came flipping to the door. Then there was muffled laughter, and a shuffle and flop.

Grey Rabbit looked at Squirrel, and Squirrel looked at Grey Rabbit.

"Who can it be?" they whispered.

Pit-pat! pit-pat! Pitter-pat! Little footsteps went flipping down the garden path, flip-flopping over the grass. Quack! Quack! Quack!

LITTLE GREY RABBIT stepped softly to the door and opened it a crack. On the doorstep lay her blue apron, rather torn and dirty, and very wet.

"Oh, how glad I am to get my little apron again," she cried, and she hung it by the fire to dry.

But the sunshade never came back. The Ducks liked it so much they wouldn't part with it.

Any day you could see them swimming down the river, one of them carrying Squirrel's sunshade, and another playing with Squirrel's ribbon bow.

THE END OF THE STORY